My Pup

by Julius Richards
illustrated by Paul Nicholls

 HOUGHTON MIFFLIN   BOSTON

I like to walk my pup up and down the street.

2

I have to tug and tug my pup away from the mud.

3

I can scrub and scrub
my pup in the tub.

4

My pup is on the rug.
I can rub and rub my pup.

5

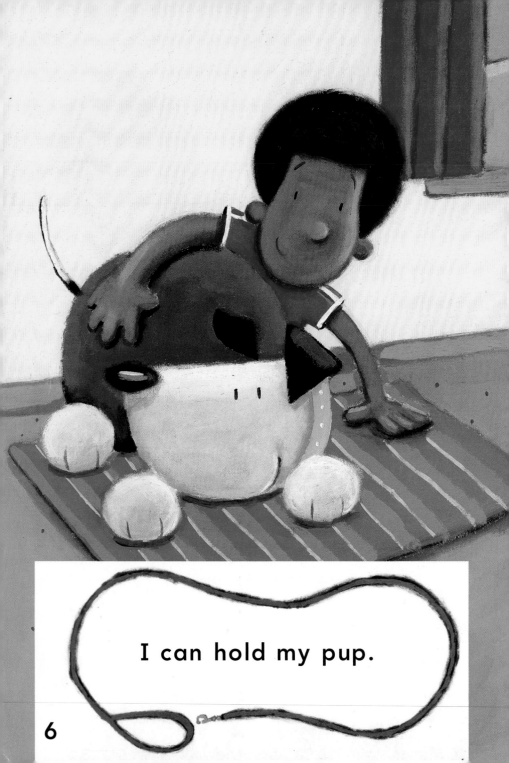

I can hold my pup.

I can hug my pup.

I love my pup,
and my pup loves me.

8